MAMMOTHS

Mammoths were large prehistoric elephants that lived in Europe, Asia and North America between 1.6 million and 10,000 years ago. A few mammoths survived in the Arctic until about 4,000 years ago. Early humans hunted mammoths for their meat, hide and tusks.

There were about 20 different types of mammoth. The woolly mammoth stood up to 2.7 m (9 ft) high and could weigh up to 9 tonnes. Woolly mammoths lived at a time when Europe was much colder than it is today. They were well adapted for living in a cold climate.

COLOUR IN THIS WOOLLY MAMMOTH.

Small ears to reduce heat loss.

ow?

DNA from frozen mammoth tissue shows that mammoths belong to the same family as modern African and Indian elephants. Scientists believe they all evolved from a common ancestor that lived in Africa about 4 million years ago.

Long tusks for clearing snow, digging plants and fighting.

Long trunk for gathering food.

Insulating layers of fat under the skin.

Thick coat for warmth.

Large body to conserve heat.

There are no written records to tell us what prehistoric times were like. We learn about them from things that have been left behind, like fossilised bones and objects made by humans. Many mammoth bodies have been discovered frozen in the icy ground in Siberia.

ICE AGES

North Polar ice cap today.

North Polar ice cap during the last Ice Age.

Prehistoric Europe was very different from how it is today. During periods called Ice Ages, the polar ice caps expanded, making the world much colder. Because so much water turned to ice, the sea level dropped. Some areas of land once separated by water joined together, making it easier for people and animals to travel.

The last Ice Age began about 1.6 million years ago and ended about 10,000 years ago. During this time, Europe was sometimes very cold, but at other times it was warmer than today. In cold periods, people and animals either had to move to warmer regions or adapt to the colder climate. As the last Ice Age ended, the climate became warmer and the sea level rose again, separating areas of land that had been joined. About 8,500 years ago Britain was cut off from mainland Europe.

did you know?

Geologists believe that the last Ice Age has not ended and that we are currently living in one of the warm periods!

HOT OR COLD?

Animals adapt to cold climates by developing larger bodies and thicker coats. Can you tell which of these animals are adapted for cold environments and which for warm ones? Which animals are still living?

Woolly mammoth

Hippopotamus

Elephant

Woolly rhino

Fallow deer

Reindeer

PREHISTORIC ANIMALS

Woolly mammoths thrived during the coldest part of the last Ice Age. With their large bodies and thick coats, they were well adapted to the cold. They lived on grassy plains known as steppes, travelling together in herds. Like modern elephants, they were herbivores (plant-eaters). They used their tusks to dig plants out from under the snow.

When the last Ice Age ended, the European climate became warmer. The plains where the mammoths had once lived were replaced by woodlands that became home to birds, deer, wild pig, wild cattle and elk. Some mammoths survived by following the retreating ice cap northwards, but their numbers decreased and by about 4,000 years ago they were extinct.

did you know?

At the peak of the last cold period about 18,000 years ago when the mammoths lived, the ice sheets in Europe were two miles thick.

Part of a spear thrower carved as a mammoth. It is about 12,500 years old.

MAMMOTH SOAP CARVING

You will need:

A bar of soap
An old pencil or ballpoint pen
A plastic knife or modelling tool

1 Use the pen or pencil to draw the outline of a mammoth on the soap. Try to fit the outline to the shape of the soap, and remember that thin pieces are likely to break off.

2 With the knife or modelling tool, carefully scrape the excess soap away.

3 Add details like eyes with the pen or pencil.

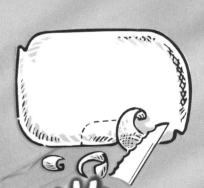

THE FIRST HUMANS

Human evolution began over 5 million years ago in Africa. By 2.5 million years ago early humans were making and using tools. They spread out of Africa, reaching northwest Europe some 500,000 years ago. These early humans lived in family groups. They built simple shelters and were able to control fire.

Early human.

In Europe, about 120,000 years ago, early humans were evolving into Neanderthals. Neanderthals were short and sturdy and their bodies were adapted for living in the cold of Ice Age Europe.

The first people like us also came from Africa, arriving in western Europe by about 35,000 years ago. Although they were not as well adapted to the cold as the Neanderthals, they were better at inventing tools and clothing that allowed them to live in the extreme cold.

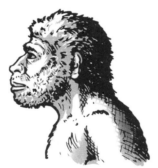

Neanderthal.

By about 28,000 years ago, fully modern humans had occupied most of Europe, and Neanderthal people gradually disappeared.

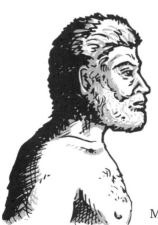

Modern human.

PRESERVED IN ICE

In 1991 a prehistoric man, nicknamed Otzi, was found frozen in ice high in the Alps. His hair, skin, clothes and shoes were all perfectly preserved. Join the dots to see how he looked when he was alive.

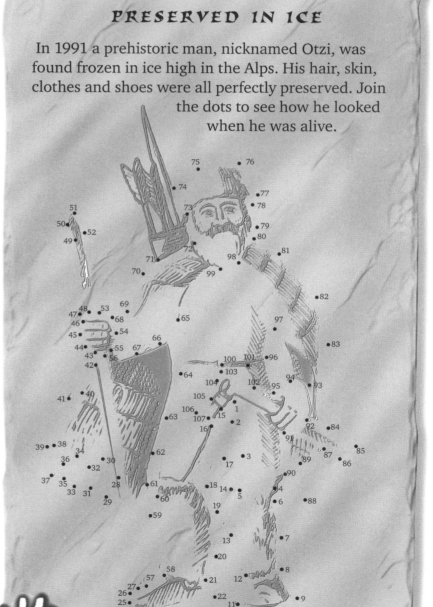

THE STONE AGE

In Europe, the prehistoric period is divided into the Stone Age, Bronze Age and Iron Age, after the material people used most often for making tools and weapons. The Stone Age itself is divided into three periods - the Palaeolithic (Old Stone Age), Mesolithic (Middle Stone Age) and Neolithic (New Stone Age). These periods are marked by changes in how people lived and got their food.

Head of a woman carved from mammoth ivory.

In the Palaeolithic period, when mammoths lived, people were always travelling in search of food. In warm periods they ate plants and roots, fruits and berries, nuts and seeds, and caught fish and shellfish. In cold periods they had to rely on hunting wild birds and animals. To help in these tasks, they made tools of stone, wood, bone and ivory. They learned to use fire for light, warmth and protection, for cooking and for hardening tools and weapons.

Flint arrowhead.

In Mesolithic times, European people found food in the forests and on the sea shores. Some began to keep animals for food, and became herders.

Neolithic people learned to grow plants for food, and instead of travelling, they lived in permanent settlements. People had more time to develop crafts like pottery and weaving, and to trade with their neighbours.

WORDSEARCH

Can you find these words hidden in the grid?

BRONZE CLAN FARMERS FIRE FISHING HORSE HUNTERS ICE AGE IRON MAMMOTH NEANDERTHAL OTZI REINDEER STONE TOOLS

W	O	M	R	E	I	N	D	E	E	R	T
N	E	A	N	D	E	R	T	H	A	L	R
A	Z	M	H	C	L	A	N	U	I	B	O
S	Q	M	D	Y	E	F	A	N	C	R	I
T	O	O	L	S	P	I	R	T	E	O	A
O	O	T	Z	I	U	R	P	E	A	N	W
N	A	H	O	R	S	E	L	R	G	Z	N
E	F	I	S	H	I	N	G	S	E	E	O
F	A	R	M	E	R	S	B	I	R	O	N

HUNTING

Palaeolithic people probably lived in family groups, hunting together and sharing the meat and hide of the animals they captured. Their prey included woolly mammoths, woolly rhinoceros, reindeer, horse, bison, wolf, fox and brown bear. These animals provided meat for food, skin for clothing and bone and antler for making tools and weapons.

The hunters may have stampeded herds of animals over cliffs, or into marshy areas or pits where they could easily be killed. The earliest hunters used wooden spears whose points had been hardened with fire, while Neanderthal hunters used stone-tipped weapons. By about 17,000 years ago modern humans had developed the spearthrower, a kind of lever that allowed a spear to be thrown with more speed, force and accuracy.

By Mesolithic times, the plains where mammoths had lived had been replaced by forests inhabited by small animals and birds. Mesolithic people developed new weapons, such as bows and arrows, to hunt these creatures. Sometimes they burnt areas of forest to create clearings where animals were attracted by new plant growth. Once inside the clearings, the animals could be caught more easily.

did you know?

Spearthrowers were used by native Australians and Inuit until quite recently. Experiments show that a spearthrower can extend the distance a spear can be thrown from 39m (129 ft) to 69m (226ft).

MAKE A FISHING GAME

You will need:

A box with a lid (a shoebox is ideal)
Coloured card
Bamboo barbecue skewers
Strong thread
Paperclips
Small magnets
PVA glue
Paints, crayons or pens
Scissors

1 Your box is the fishing pond. Colour the inside blue (you might like to add some water plants) and decorate the outside.

2 Cut fish shapes from the coloured card. Your fish should be about 5 cm (2 in) long, and you will need at least twenty fish.

3 Decorate the fish, then gently push a paperclip onto the front of each one. Make sure the loop of the paperclip sticks out. You can add a dab of glue to each fish to hold the paperclip in place.

FISHING

The first humans probably collected shellfish along shorelines and in rockpools, and speared or clubbed larger fish. By 14,000 years ago, modern humans learned to make fishing harpoons with antler tips and wooden shafts. Some tips had a hole to attach a line, and these were only loosely fixed to the shaft. When the hunter speared a fish or seal, the tip of the harpoon stuck into the prey and came off its shaft. The catch could then be pulled to shore using the line.

Rock drawing of people in a boat fishing with hooks and lines.

Towards the end of the Ice Age, people fished using lines with hooks or gorges. A gorge is a piece of bone or antler with a sharp point at either end. A line is tied to the middle, and the gorge is hidden inside a piece of bait. When a fish swallows the bait, the gorge sticks in its throat and it can be hauled in.

Fish gorge and hook.

Harpoon.

Fishing nets and fish traps were also used by about 10,000 years ago. Fish traps were long baskets with a wide opening at one end and a narrow opening at the other. They were placed in rivers and on seashores, with the wide end facing the flow, so that fish swimming into the trap were unable to escape.

Fish trap.

4 Now make a fishing rod for each player:

Take a bamboo skewer and snip off the pointed tip. About 1 cm (½ in) from the cut end, run the scissors around the skewer to make a groove.

Take a piece of thread about 25 cm (10 in) long, wrap it around the groove a couple of times, then tie it in place. Add a dab of glue to stop the thread coming undone.

Tie a magnet to the other end of the thread.

5 To play the game, place all the fish in the pond, and take turns to catch fish. The game is over when the pool is empty, and the winner is the player with the most fish.

Store the rods and fish inside the box to play the game another day.

STONE TOOLS AND WEAPONS

Before prehistoric people discovered metals they used stone, bone, antler, ivory and wood to make tools and weapons. The first stone tools, made in Africa more than 2 million years ago, were 'choppers' – pebbles chipped away at one end to form a sharp cutting edge.

Flint hand axe.

Pebble chopper.

Over time humans became better at working stone, particularly flint, which breaks to produce useful razor-sharp flakes. The oldest flint tools found in Europe were made about 500,000 years ago. These 'hand axes' were general-purpose tools with a sharp point.

PAPIER-MÂCHÈ FLINTS

You will need:

Wallpaper paste
PVA glue
Old newspapers
Cardboard tubes
String
Measuring jug
Plastic container with airtight lid
Mixing spoon
Tray for drying

1 Following the instructions on the packet, mix up a small amount of the wallpaper paste in the plastic container.

2 Tear some newspaper into tiny pieces (1 - 2 cm, ½ - 1 in across) and mix it into the paste. Keep adding pieces of paper until the mixture looks like lumpy porridge.

3 Take a small handful of the mixture. Holding it over the bowl, squeeze out any excess paste.

4 Shape the mixture into the flint shape you want, then place it on the tray to dry overnight in a warm place.

5 You can make larger flints, like axeheads, by building them up in layers. If you seal the plastic container carefully, the papier-maché mixture will last for several days. Make sure that each layer is dry before adding the next one.

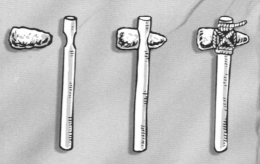

6 To make an axe, cut a slit through one end of a long cardboard tube. Cover the openings with PVA glue, and push the axehead into place. When the glue has dried, wrap string around the axehead and handle to hold them together.

Flint core and blades.

By 35,000 years ago in Europe Palaeolithic stoneworkers discovered that by first making a specially shaped core, many blades could be flaked from a single piece of flint by striking it with a hammer made of soft stone or antler. This technique made it possible to create specialised tools such as blades and scrapers.

In the Mesolithic and Neolithic periods, flint-working ('knapping') techniques became more advanced. Flint points were used to tip spears and arrows. Blades and axe heads were fitted to handles made of wood and antler. Neolithic people also made polished stone axeheads.

PREHISTORIC ART

In Europe, by about 34,000 years ago, Palaeolithic people had begun to draw pictures on to pieces of stone, bone and antler as well as the walls of rock shelters. They drew and carved figures of humans and animals as well as signs, symbols and patterns.

Cave painting of animals.

Between about 34,000 and 10,000 years ago, the interiors of caves were sometimes decorated with painted or modelled figures of animals and humans. The caves may have been special places for religious or hunting rituals. In some caves, people recorded their visits by making outlines of their hands. They did this by blowing paint onto the cave wall through hollow bird bones.

Modelled clay bison.

Outline hand prints.

Prehistoric paints were made from natural colours mixed with animal fat. Charcoal was used for black and iron minerals for reds, yellows and browns. The artists made their paint into crayons, or painted with their fingers, pieces of animal fur, sticks or feathers. The caves were dark, so artists used stone lamps filled with animal fat that burned like candles.

did you know?

At Rouffignac in France a cave system called the "Cave of a Hundred Mammoths" contains hundreds of pictures of animals painted 12,000 years ago.

MAMMOTH CAVE PAINTING

1 Tear a piece of card from the box, crumple it a little, then smooth it out again to give a rough surface for your painting.

You will need:
Paints: red, black, brown and yellow
Small sticks and twigs, feathers
Brown cardboard box

2 Using a twig, a feather or your fingers, paint mammoths and other animals on to the card. Try drawing around your hand to make hand prints.

9

SHELTER

Just like us, prehistoric humans needed protection from the weather. Palaeolithic people were often on the move. Sometimes they occupied caves and rock shelters, and at other times they built huts or tents from branches covered with animal skins.

Cave shelter.

Between 20,000 and 30,000 years ago, the mammoth hunters of Eastern Europe and Russia built large huts from mammoth remains. Measuring up to 35m (115 ft) long and 18m (60 ft) wide, the huts were set into the ground to keep out the wind. The walls were built of mammoth bones and jaws, the roof from the curved tusks covered with skin.

Hut made of mammoth bones.

Some Mesolithic people had permanent homes, but most spent a lot of time in temporary hunting camps. By Neolithic times, more people had settled down, building permanent dwellings of stone or wood covered with mud, and roofed with animal skins or thatch.

Neolithic house.

WHAT'S IN THE CAVE?

Unscramble the words to help this clan find a safe place to stay.

A
ESRAB

B
VOSWEL

C
SESDRIP

D
OLNIS

CLOTHING AND JEWELLERY

To survive in a cold climate, humans must wear clothes to keep them warm and dry, but remains of Palaeolithic clothing are rare. Early humans and Neanderthals probably wore simple clothing made of animal skins.

Modern humans used animal sinews and bone and antler needles to sew the skins into warm, weatherproof clothing. Figures carved from mammoth tusk in Siberia 15,000 years ago show people wearing hooded clothes. They would also have worn boots, leggings, jackets, hats, and maybe mittens.

Prehistoric people also wore jewellery. Bracelets and pendants were carved from bone, antler and mammoth ivory. Shells, pebbles and animal teeth were strung together to make belts and necklaces. From Neolithic times, gold and copper were also used to make ornaments.

In Neolithic times, people discovered how to spin plant fibres and animal wool into yarn that could be woven into cloth. However, much clothing was still made of animal skins. Otzi, the 5,000-year-old alpine ice mummy, was dressed in a bearskin cap, a knee-length goatskin coat, a grass cloak, goatskin leggings, a calfskin belt, a goatskin loincloth and a pair of leather shoes stuffed with grass to keep his feet warm.

MAKE A STONE AGE NECKLACE

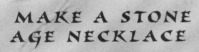

You will need:

Pierced shells or pebbles
A leather thong or bootlace

Next time you're at the beach, look out for shells and pebbles with holes worn in them. Threaded on to a leather thong or bootlace, they make a great necklace. You can use just one shell or pebble to make a pendant, or group lots together.

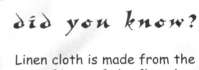

Bronze pins.

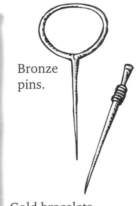

Gold bracelets.

DOMESTIC ANIMALS

From about 12,000 years ago, humans began to tame, or 'domesticate', certain animals. The first domesticated animal was probably the dog, which is descended from the Asiatic wolf. Dogs could help with hunting and act as guards, and were useful for rounding up herds of wild or domestic animals.

Neolithic people kept animals for their meat, milk, skins and wool. Large animals like cattle, horses and reindeer were also used for transport and to help with heavy farm work such as ploughing. Sheep, goats and pigs were domesticated about 10,000 years ago, horses about 6,000 years ago and cattle about 5,000 years ago.

Sheep, goats and cattle eat a lot of plants, and must be moved regularly to new grazing places before they run out of food. In summer, lowland pastures could be very dry, so people took their herds into the mountains where it was cooler and wetter. In the winter they led the animals back to the valleys before it became too cold. Some people spent their lives travelling with their herds; others built permanent homes and only spent part of the year living in temporary camps with their animals.

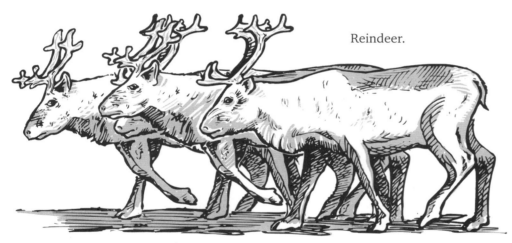
Reindeer.

LOST SHEEP

Six sheep have gone missing in the bushes. Can you help to find them?

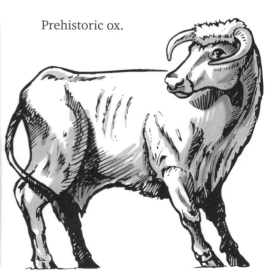
Prehistoric ox.

PLANTS AND FARMING

Plant foods have always been important for humans, both for nutrition and for medicine. Palaeolithic people collected plants, berries, nuts and seeds, and made tools for digging up roots.

In Mesolithic times the climate was warmer and wetter. Woodlands provided a greater variety of plant foods, including wild raspberries, pears, apples and hazelnuts. Some of these foods could be dried and kept for the winter. Mesolithic people probably looked after the wild plants they used. Burning areas of woodland enriched the soil and encouraged certain plants to grow.

Hoe for digging the ground and sickle for cutting grain.

By Neolithic times, people had learned to grow wheat and barley using seed saved from the previous year's harvest. They began to stay in one place to tend their crops. To help the plants grow, they cleared the land and broke up the soil before sowing the seed. Tools like hoes and ox-drawn ploughs made these jobs easier.

GROWING FOOD FROM SEEDS

You will need:
A small flowerpot or a clean, empty yoghurt pot with a hole punched in the bottom
Soil or compost
Cress seeds

1 Fill the pot with moist soil or compost.

2 Sprinkle a little cress seed into the pot, and press it lightly into the soil or compost.

3 Stand the pot on a saucer and place it on a sunny windowsill. Keep the soil or compost moist, and in a few days you will have a crop of cress to add to your salads!

POTS
AND PANS

From the earliest times, prehistoric people invented things to make their daily lives easier. Palaeolithic people made tools to help them to hunt and fish, build houses, make clothing and prepare food. Baskets were woven from reeds and young branches to make traps and containers.

Decorated clay pots.

Staying in one place meant that Neolithic people had more time for making things and could own heavy or fragile objects. Pots for storage and cooking were made by coiling rolls of clay into a hollow shape, then smoothing over the surface. The finished pots were baked on open fires to make them hard and waterproof.

Neolithic people also learned to shape soft metals like copper and gold into small objects like pins and beads. Although copper is easy to work, it is hard to keep sharp, so flint was still used for most tools and weapons. In the Bronze Age, metalworkers learned to extract metals like copper and tin from ore-bearing rocks. They also discovered that adding a little tin to copper made bronze, a much harder metal, useful for tools, cooking vessels and weapons.

MAKE A PREHISTORIC POT

You will need:

Self-hardening clay
Plastic knife or modelling tool
String

1 Take a piece of clay and make it into a ball by rolling it between your hands.

2 Push your thumb into the middle of the ball and squeeze the clay towards the edges to make a hollow base.

3 Take a smaller piece of clay and roll it between your hands to make a long, thin sausage shape.

4 Coil the clay sausage around the edge of the hollow base, and press it into place.

5 Make more sausages and use them to build up the sides of your pot.

6 When your pot is the shape you want, use your knife or modelling tool to smooth the inside and outside.

7 Prehistoric people used to decorate their pots by pressing their fingernails or pieces of string into the clay. See what patterns you can make on your pot.

PREHISTORIC MONUMENTS

Early Neolithic people built the first tombs and monuments in Europe. Neolithic and Bronze Age people buried their dead under earth mounds called barrows. Neolithic barrows often had stone burial chambers. The 4,500-year-old 'long barrow' at West Kennet in England is about 100 m (328 ft) long, with five chambers leading off a central passage. It contained the remains of fifty people.

Late Neolithic and Bronze Age people also built henges (circular areas of land surrounded by a ditch and an earth bank) and circles of wooden posts or stones. Some of these may have had religious uses. Others seem to have worked like calendars, measuring time by tracking the movements of the sun and moon. This information was important for Neolithic farmers and herders, who needed to know the right time to plant their crops or move their animals.

did you know?

Neolithic and Bronze Age people often cremated their dead. Their ashes were buried in special pots called urns.

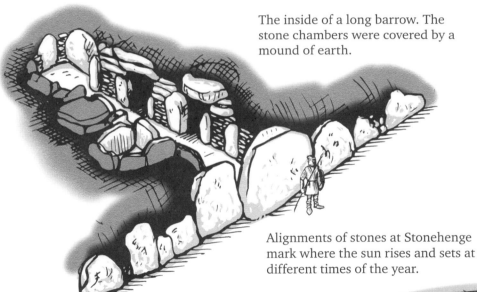

The inside of a long barrow. The stone chambers were covered by a mound of earth.

Alignments of stones at Stonehenge mark where the sun rises and sets at different times of the year.

One of the most famous prehistoric monuments is Stonehenge in Wiltshire, England, which began about 5,000 years ago as a circular bank and ditch with a ring of wooden posts. Over the next 1,000 years the stone monument seen today was built, using local sandstone boulders (sarsens) and Welsh bluestones.

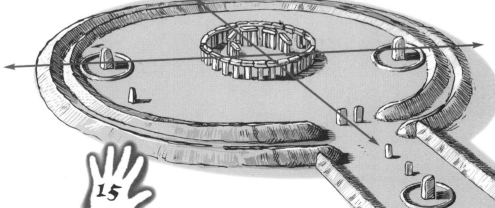

STONEHENGE CHALLENGE

How many words of three or more letters can you make from the word STONEHENGE using each letter only once?
We found 44 – can you beat us?

BOATS AND TRAVEL

Palaeolithic people had to walk most of the time, but some must have built rafts to cross rivers and the sea. By Mesolithic times, people were using log canoes made from hollowed-out tree trunks for fishing and for travelling along coastlines and rivers.

THE BEWILDERED BOATMAN

Can you help the boatman guide his craft safely to shore?

Mesolithic boat builders.

While travelling, people probably collected things like medicinal plants and wild honey, and hunted animals for skins which they could trade with people on their journeys. As it became easier for people to get around they were more able to trade with their neighbours for the things they needed.

ANSWERS

Page 2 Mammoths, reindeer and woolly rhinos are adapted for the cold. Elephants, deer and hippos are adapted for warm weather. Mammoths and woolly rhinos are extinct.

Page 5 Word grid

Page 10

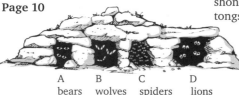

A	B	C	D
bears	wolves	spiders	lions

Page 15
ego, eon, get, got, hen, hog, hot, net, not, one, see, set, son, sot, ten, toe, ton, gene, gent, gone, gosh, hens, hone, hose, host, nest, none, nose, note, seen, sent, shot, song, then, tone, ghost, henge, sheen, sheet, shone, stone, thong, tongs, sonnet.

Page 12 Sheep

Page 16 Maze

© 2004 The Trustees of the British Museum

Published in 2004 by British Museum Press, A division of The British Museum Company Ltd, 46 Bloomsbury Street, London WC1B 3QQ

ISBN 0 7141 3016 7
A catalogue record for this book is available from the British Library.

Delia Pemberton and Daniel Pemberton have asserted the right to be identified as the authors of this work.

Designed and illustrated by HERRING BONE DESIGN/ David Gillingwater
Printed and bound by Oriental Press